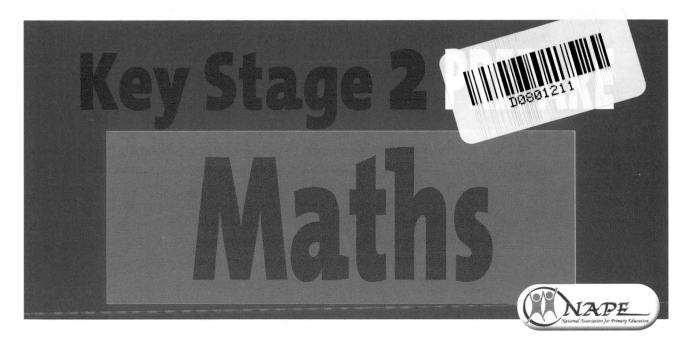

Contents

AUTHOR: Camilla de la Bédoyère
EDITORIAL: John Cattermole, Sarah Goulding, Julia Rolf
DESIGN: Dave Jones, Mike Spender
ILLUSTRATORS: David Benham and Charlie-Anne Turner of Graham-Cameron Illustration
PRODUCTION: Chris Herbert, Claire Walker

COMMISSIONING EDITOR: Polly Willis
PUBLISHER AND CREATIVE DIRECTOR: Nick Wells

3 Book Pack ISBN 1-84451-111-1   Book ISBN 1-84451-174-X
6 Book Pack ISBN 1-84451-137-5   Book ISBN 1-84451-156-1

First published in 2004

A copy of the CIP data for this book is available from the British Library upon request.

Created and produced by
FLAME TREE PUBLISHING
Crabtree Hall,
Crabtree Lane,
Fulham, London SW6 6TY
United Kingdom
www.flametreepublishing.com

Flame Tree Publishing is part of The Foundry Creative Media Co. Ltd.

© The Foundry Creative Media Co. Ltd, 2004

Printed in Croatia

Foreword

Sometimes when I am crossing the playground on my way to visit a primary school I pass young children playing at schools. There is always a stern authoritarian little teacher at the front laying down the law to the unruly group of children in the pretend class. This puzzles me a little because the school I am visiting is very far from being like the children's play. Where do they get this Victorian view of what school is like? Perhaps it's handed down from generation to generation through the genes. Certainly they don't get it from their primary school. Teachers today are more often found alongside their pupils, who are learning by actually doing things for themselves, rather than merely listening and obeying instructions.

Busy children, interested and involved in their classroom reflect what we know about how they learn. Of course they learn from teachers but most of all they learn from their experience of life and their life is spent both in and out of school. Indeed, if we compare the impact upon children of even the finest schools and teachers, we find that three or four times as great an impact is made by the reality of children's lives outside the school. That reality has the parent at the all important centre. No adult can have so much impact, for good or ill, as the young child's mother or father.

This book, and others in the series, are founded on the sure belief that the great majority of parents want to help their children grow and learn and that teachers are keen to support them. The days when parents were kept at arm's length from schools are long gone and over the years we have moved well beyond the white line painted on the playground across which no parent must pass without an appointment. Now parents move freely in and out of schools and very often are found in the classrooms backing up the teachers. Both sides of the partnership know how important it is that children should be challenged and stimulated both in and out of school.

Perhaps the most vital part of this book is where parents and children are encouraged to develop activities beyond those offered on the page. The more the children explore and use the ideas and techniques we want them to learn, the more they will make new knowledge of their very own. It's not just getting the right answer, it's growing as a person through gaining skill in action and not only in books. The best way to learn is to live.

I remember reading a story to a group of nine year old boys. The story was about soldiers and of course the boys, bloodthirsty as ever, were hanging on my every word. I came to the word khaki and I asked the group "What colour is khaki?" One boy was quick to answer. "Silver," he said, "It's silver." "Silver?" I queried. "Yes," he said with absolute confidence, "Silver, my Dad's car key is silver." Now I reckon I'm a pretty good teller of stories to children but when it came down to it, all my dramatic reading of a gripping story gave way immediately to the power of the boy's experience of life. That meant so much more to him, as it does to all children.

JOHN COE
General Secretary, National Association for Primary Education (NAPE).

Parents and teachers work together in NAPE to improve the quality of learning and teaching in primary schools. We campaign hard for a better deal for children at the vital early stage of their education upon which later success depends. We are always pleased to hear from parents.

NAPE, Moulton College, Moulton, Northampton, NN3 7RR,
Telephone: 01604 647 646 Web: www.nape.org.uk

Maths is one of six books in the Prepare (Key Stage Two) Series. These books have been devised to help you support your child as they move into their final years at Primary School. During Years Five and Six, children's attention is focused on the upcoming SATs exams, which they will sit in the summer of Year Six.

Through a series of activities and questions, your child will be introduced to topics that they can expect to cover during Year Five, as laid out in the National Numeracy Strategy. The Strategy covers five broad areas:

- Numbers and the Number System
- Calculations
- Solving Problems
- Handling Data
- Measures, Shape and Space.

The curriculum allows for some overlap between years to accommodate different levels of ability. In some instances, therefore, your child will be will be able to revise topics they have already studied, in preparation for a new school year.

- Each topic begins with an introduction, **Parents Start Here**, which will give you more information and will explain its relevance or relationship to other topics in the Curriculum.

- Boxes labelled **Activity** appear throughout the book. They direct the child towards other activities, to be conducted away from the book.

- The questions and activities in the book aim to introduce new ideas and concepts in a fun way, but your child will benefit from your involvement too.

Prepare a 'maths box' for your child, containing essential equipment for maths. Include a ruler, pencils, scissors, coloured pencils, a protractor, a pair of compasses, squared paper, a calculator and counters. A maths box like this can be useful for tackling homework too.

There is a checklist at the end of the book; use this to motivate your child and help them to see how much learning they have achieved.

Parents Start Here...

During Year Five, children consolidate their knowledge of numbers and number order. They are targeted with reading whole numbers to at least 10,000 and being able to use the vocabulary of comparing and ordering numbers.

Number Cards

$=$ equals sign: means 'the same as'.
$<$ less than sign: means the number to the left is less than the number to the right e.g. $3 < 5$.
$>$ more than sign: means the number to the left is more than the number to the right e.g. $5 > 3$.

Tick the statements that are true:

$482 < 890$ ☑

$10{,}854 = 10{,}000 + 854$ ☑

$0.1 < 0.01$ ☒

$98.5 > 985$ ☒

$56 = 8 \times 8$ ☒

Write a number that is 1000 more than 402: 1402

Write the number in words:

Oneth One thousand four hundred and two

Here are four number cards:

Copy the digits on to four pieces of paper to make your own number cards and rearrange them to answer the following questions.
Give as many correct answers as you can find:

A whole number < 7458	A whole number > 5874
5478	8457

What is the smallest whole number you can make with these four digits? 4578

What is the largest whole number you can make with these four digits? 8754

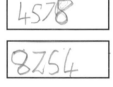

FUN FACT!

There can be up to 40,000,000,000 (40 billion) locusts in a single swarm.

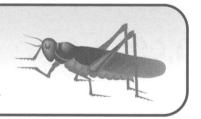

TRY THIS ## Activity

Make your own digit cards like the ones featured here. Rearrange them to make the largest and smallest numbers you can.

Check Your Progress!
Number Cards
Turn to page 32 and put a tick next to what you have just learned.

Parents Start Here...

In Year Five, children are taught how to measure and calculate the perimeters of rectangles and regular polygons.

String's The Thing

Measure this piece of string with your ruler:

_____9_____ cm

The piece of string has now been bent to make a triangle.

Measure each side of the triangle:

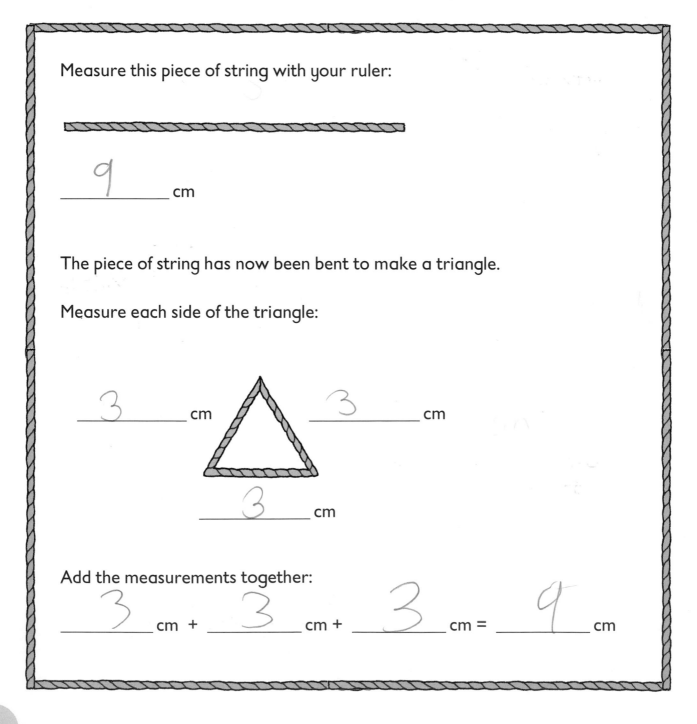

_____3_____ cm   _____3_____ cm

_____3_____ cm

Add the measurements together:

_____3_____ cm + _____3_____ cm + _____3_____ cm = _____9_____ cm

Perimeter: the distance all the way round a flat (2-D) shape.

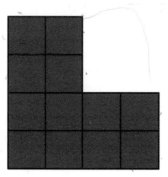

2cm

Each side of this hexagon measures 2 cm:

To calculate its perimeter you just need to add up the lengths of each side:

_2_ + _2_ + _2_ + _2_ + _2_ + _2_ = _12_ cm

Work out the perimeter of this shape.

The sides of each square are 1 cm.

The perimeter is __16__ cm

FUN FACT!

The perimeter of a circle is known as its circumference.

TRY THIS Activity

Use squared paper to draw some of your own shapes and work out the perimeters. Draw shapes with straight lines. If you draw shapes with curved lines you could measure them using a piece of string, then measure the string.

Check Your Progress!
String's The Thing ☐

Turn to page 32 and put a tick next to what you have just learned.

Top Tip!
Go through this page as often as you like until your child understands it fully.

Parents Start Here...

In order to be able to complete mental calculations quickly, children need to know certain number facts and be confident of them. Help your child practise counting forwards and backwards in steps of a constant size, e.g. "Start at 60 and count back in sixes as far as you can go..."

Biggest And Best

Multiple: the numbers in a multiplication table e.g. multiples of six are 6, 12, 18 etc.

Colour in all of the multiples of six to reveal the name of the longest snake in the world:

5	24	22	12	36	26	28	66	32	48	52	40	56	54
t	p	i	y	t	s	p	h	v	o	i	p	r	n

The name of the longest snake in the world is _Python_

The longest snake ever found measured a whopping ten metres!

Colour in all of the multiples of seven to reveal the name of the bird with the greatest wingspan: _albatross_

21	35	27	70	7	37	77	44	63	22	56	49	34	14
a	l	r	b	a	o	t	b	r	i	o	s	n	s

One of these birds was found to have a wingspan of 3.63 metres. Measure it – that's huge!

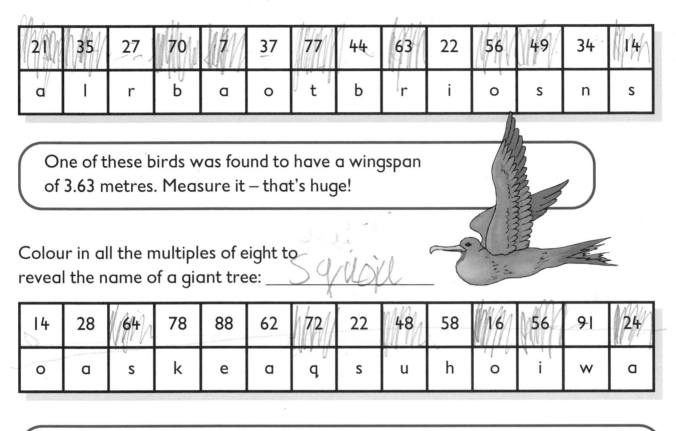

Colour in all the multiples of eight to reveal the name of a giant tree: _sequoia_

14	28	64	78	88	62	72	22	48	58	16	56	91	24
o	a	s	k	e	a	q	s	u	h	o	i	w	a

One of these trees has reached 84 metres in height. They can live for over 4000 years.

TRY THIS

Activity

Try this game when you are on a long journey. The first player thinks of one number between 100 and 10,000 and a second number that is less than ten. Starting with the big number, players take it in turns to take away the smaller number. The first one to make a mistake is out. See if you can get all the way back to zero!

Check Your Progress!

Biggest And Best

Turn to page 32 and put a tick next to what you have just learned.

Parents Start Here...

The activity here requires children to carry out quick mental addition and subtraction. They need to add several numbers together and use known addition and subtraction facts to find the answers. Mental calculation strategies are important: methods include adding hundreds first, then tens and then units, and identifying near doubles, e.g. 1.5 + 1.6.

Sports Day

When you add up a list of numbers in your head you can do it in different ways:
1. Add up the tens first, then the units and add the totals.
2. Round the numbers up, or down, to the nearest large number. You can then add them and make the adjustments afterwards.

Use mental maths strategies to answer these questions.

It is Sports Day at Park Hill Primary School.

Ravinder ran around the field 12 times, Raj ran round it 11 times, Mary ran round it 15 times and Moko ran round it 9 times.

How many times did the children run round the field altogether? ____47____

James did three jumps in the long jump: 1.20 m, 1.32 m and 99 cm. What was the total distance he jumped? ___3.5cm___

10

When you subtract in your head you can do it in different ways:
1. You can chop the numbers into tens and units before you do the calculation.
2. You can round the numbers up or down first, so you are dealing with easier numbers. You do your subtractions, then make the adjustments.
3. You can add up from the smaller number.

Julie won the high jump: she jumped 97 cm. Jasmine came second, jumping 88 cm.

What was the difference in the heights? ___9cm___

FUN FACT!

Marathons are long-distance running races that cover 42.2 km.

Tom ran round the track in 2 minutes 14 seconds.
He wants to run it in 1 minute 55 seconds.
What is the difference in these two times? ~~2mins~~ 9secs

TRY THIS ## Activity

Try doing the long jump in the garden or park.
You can use a measuring tape to record your scores.

Check Your Progress!

Sports Day ☐

Turn to page 32 and put a tick next to what you have just learned.

Top Tip! Learning is fun, so if your child is tired, let them come back to this when they are fresh.

Parents Start Here...

When children learn how to organise data in tables and charts, they can see the importance of choosing the best format. Show your child how one set of data can be presented in different ways. If possible, practise making tables and charts together using a computer.

School Journeys

Children in Year Five at Cottage Mill Primary were asked how they travelled to school. The results were added up and put in this bar chart.

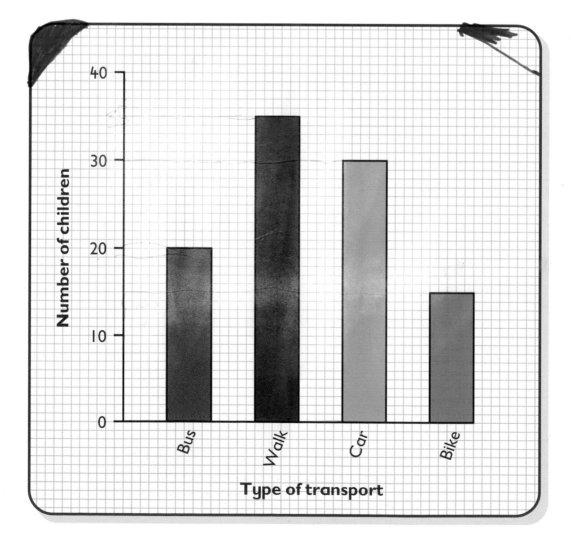

How many children walk to school? _____35_____

How many more children walk to school than go by car? _____S_____

What is the least popular way of getting to school? _____Bike_____

The local Council of Cottage Mill Town wants to get more cars off the road.
How do you think they could encourage children to travel to school in other ways?

If you go by car and bus you are poloting
the world.

_____

_____

How many children took part in the survey altogether? _____100_____

FUN FACT!

The first bicycle was seen in Paris in 1791.

Activity

Conduct your own survey. You could find out eye colour,
favourite colour, favourite band or favourite TV
programme. Once you have collected your results you
can put them into a bar chart. Look in newspapers for
bar charts: they are often used to show data.

Check Your Progress!
School Journeys

Turn to page 32 and put a tick next to what you have just learned.

Top Tip!
If your child loses concentration here, let them take a break.

Parents Start Here...

Measuring area in cm^2 is a key objective for Year Five. Show your child the length and width of rectangular objects around the home. Help them to work out, for example, the surface area of a door or table top.

Square It

Area: the amount of space taken up by a flat (2-D) object.

Each side of the square measures 1 cm. Its area is 1 cm^2

How many square centimetres (cm^2) are in each shape?

1 cm

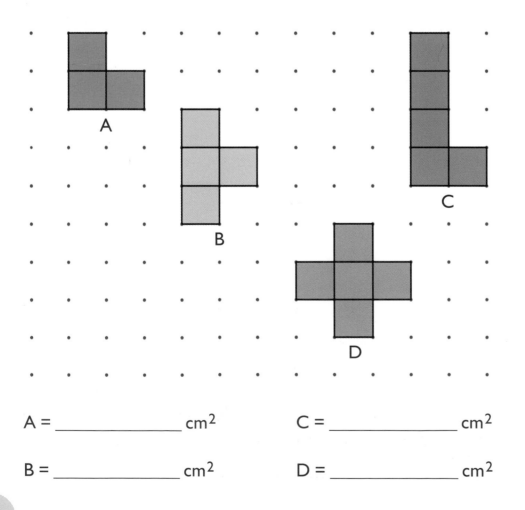

A

B

C

D

A = _____ cm^2 C = _____ cm^2

B = _____ cm^2 D = _____ cm^2

You can measure the area of a rectangle by multiplying the length by the width (breadth).

length x width = area of a rectangle

4 cm x 2 cm = 8 cm^2

2 cm width

4 cm length

Calculate the areas of these shapes:

Tip: your first step is to measure the sides using a ruler.

A

_____ cm^2

B

_____ cm^2

C

_____ cm^2

F

_____ cm^2

D

_____ cm^2

E

_____ cm^2

FUN FACT!

An estimated 70 per cent of the Earth's surface area is covered in water.

TRY THIS

Activity

Cut out some rectangles from paper. Now can you cut each one to make two identical triangles? Use this information to help you work out a way of calculating the area of one of the triangles.

Check Your Progress!

Square It

Turn to page 32 and put a tick next to what you have just learned.

Parents Start Here...

During Year Four children are taught decimal notation and learn that a fraction, such as $\frac{1}{2}$, and a decimal, such as 0.5, are equivalent. In Year Five they continue to develop this concept and practise finding equivalent fractions. Decimals can easily confuse children who are at the early stages of learning about fractions. Simple number lines, like the ones used here, can be a useful way to remind your child of the relative values of the digits in decimals.

A Fraction Of...

Equivalent fractions: fractions that mean the same thing, e.g. $\frac{2}{4} = \frac{1}{2}$

whole	
$\frac{1}{2}$	$\frac{1}{2}$

$\frac{1}{4}$	$\frac{1}{4}$	$\frac{1}{4}$	$\frac{1}{4}$

$\frac{1}{8}$	$\frac{1}{8}$	$\frac{1}{8}$	$\frac{1}{8}$	$\frac{1}{8}$	$\frac{1}{8}$	$\frac{1}{8}$	$\frac{1}{8}$

$$\frac{1}{4} = \frac{2}{8}$$

whole	
$\frac{1}{2}$	$\frac{1}{2}$

$\frac{1}{3}$	$\frac{1}{3}$	$\frac{1}{3}$

$\frac{1}{6}$	$\frac{1}{6}$	$\frac{1}{6}$	$\frac{1}{6}$	$\frac{1}{6}$	$\frac{1}{6}$

$$\frac{2}{6} = \frac{1}{3}$$

Look at the charts to answer these questions:

$$\frac{1}{4} = \frac{\square}{8} \qquad \frac{4}{6} = \frac{\square}{3} \qquad \frac{2}{4} = \frac{\square}{2} \qquad \frac{1}{2} = \frac{\square}{6}$$

Decimals are just another way of talking about numbers between whole numbers. Fractions do the same thing, but in a different way.

This number line has got decimals and fractions written on it.
The number 1 has been divided into tenths:

0	0.1	0.2	0.3	0.4	0.5	0.6	0.7	0.8	0.9	1.0
	$\frac{1}{10}$	$\frac{2}{10}$	$\frac{3}{10}$	$\frac{4}{10}$	$\frac{5}{10}$	$\frac{6}{10}$	$\frac{7}{10}$	$\frac{8}{10}$	$\frac{9}{10}$	$\frac{10}{10}$

Write an equivalent fraction for $\frac{5}{10}$: $\quad \frac{5}{10} = \frac{\boxed{}}{2}$

Look on the number line to find what decimal number is equivalent to $\frac{3}{10}$: _____

Write the decimals on the number lines:

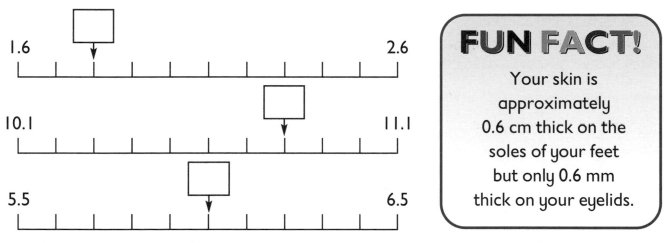

1.6 $\quad\boxed{}$ 2.6

10.1 $\quad\boxed{}$ 11.1

5.5 $\quad\boxed{}$ 6.5

FUN FACT!

Your skin is approximately 0.6 cm thick on the soles of your feet but only 0.6 mm thick on your eyelids.

TRY THIS

Home Learn

Look on a ruler and find ten centimetres. Ten centimetres is divided into tenths: one centimetre each. Each centimetre is divided into another ten. How many millimetres are there in ten centimetres?

Check Your Progress!
A Fraction Of... $\boxed{}$
Turn to page 32 and put a tick next to what you have just learned.

Top Tip!
Remember to give your child lots of praise – they will work so much better.

Parents Start Here...

During Year Five, children are targeted with developing written methods for adding and subtracting two integers (whole numbers) less than 10,000. The first method taught for addition involves chopping, or partitioning, numbers into hundreds, tens and units and totalling these separately. The first method taught for subtraction is normally 'repeated addition', whereby the child keeps adding on to the smaller number.

Chopping And Chunking

When you add two numbers you can chop them up into hundreds, tens and units to make it easier.

Example:

```
    486
  + 223
  -----
    600    add the hundreds first (400 + 200)
    100    add the tens next (80 + 20)
      9    add the units next (6 + 3)
  -----
    709
```

Do these additions:

736	21.9	67.3	759	552.5	3.25
+ 642	+ 132.3	+ 24.1	+ 16.7	+ 89.3	+ 8.96

FUN FACT! The planet Saturn is 95 times larger than the Earth and it has more than 20 moons.

When you subtract one number from another you can do it by adding the difference.

Example:
$$683$$
$$- \quad 241$$

250	+ 9	add 9 to 241 to make 250
650	+ 400	add 400 to 250 to make 650. Nearly there!
683	+ 33	add 33 to 650 to make 683
		add these to find the difference: 442

683 – 241 = 442

> The great thing about this method is you can add big chunks or small chunks each time – it's up to you.

Use this method to do these subtractions:

963	735	862	1049
- 693	- 342	- 97	- 861

FUN FACT!

The planet Venus is nearer to the Sun than Earth and is much hotter. The temperature on Venus can reach 462°C.

TRY THIS

Activity

Use your calculator to find some negative numbers.
What is the smallest number you can make on a calculator?

Check Your Progress!
Chopping And Chunking ☐

Turn to page 32 and put a tick next to what you have just learned.

Parents Start Here...

Children in Year Five are targeted with recognising perpendicular and parallel lines.

Lines And Corners

Parallel lines: two lines that can travel on forever, side by side but never touching.

Perpendicular lines: two lines that meet at a right angle.

A rectangle has two pairs of parallel lines.
One pair has been identified for you.
Use the symbol to mark the other pair.

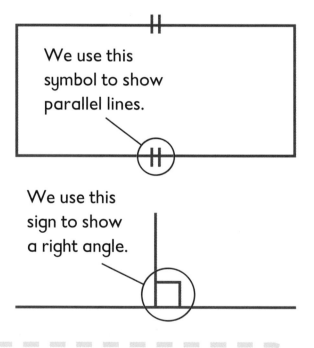

We use this symbol to show parallel lines.

These two lines are perpendicular.

We use this sign to show a right angle.

Draw another two perpendicular lines:

Tick the shapes that have parallel lines and mark the lines with the correct symbol. Use the right angle symbol to show where you have found right angles.

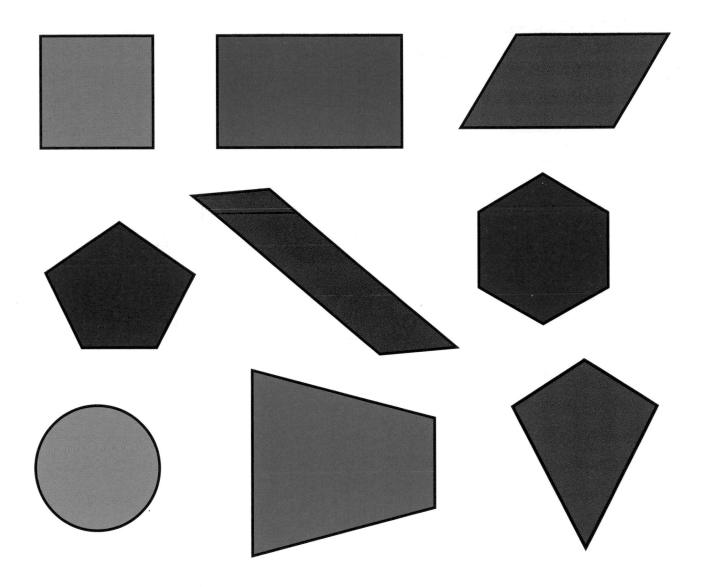

 **Activity**

If you look at simple 3-D shapes you should be able to identify parallel faces on some of them. Try looking at a box to give you an idea.

Check Your Progress!
Lines And Corners
Turn to page 32 and put a tick next to what you have just learned.

Parents Start Here...

Always encourage your child to approximate an answer before they begin multiplying on paper. This will help prevent silly errors. They can do this by rounding the numbers up, or down, and then carrying out mental strategies.

Best Of Times

The first step to multiplying on paper is to partition the numbers.

357 x 45 =	357	=	300
			50
			7

| | 45 | = | 40 |
| | | | 5 |

Partition the numbers to complete the table:

	thousands	hundreds	tens	units
4672	4000	600	70	2
562				
66				
486				
87				
1023				

Once you have partitioned the numbers you can put them into a grid:

X	300	50	7
40			
5			

22

You can then do the multiplications in each section of the grid and put the answers in.

40 x 300 = 12,000   5 x 300 = 1500
40 x 50 = 2000   5 x 50 = 250
40 x 7 = 280   5 x 7 = 35

Add the totals of each column to get your answer:

X	300	50	7
40	12,000	2000	280
5	1500	250	35

      13,500   + 2250   + 315 = 16,065

> What would happen if you added the totals of the rows, instead of the totals of the columns? Try it and see.

Try this multiplication on a separate sheet of paper:

562 x 66 =

FUN FACT!

If you travelled to the centre of the Milky Way it would take you 30,000 years, even travelling at the speed of light (1,049 million km/hour).

Activity

The best way to get the hang of this method of multiplication is to practise it lots of times. Once you know it, teach it to an adult. Adults know a much more complicated, but faster, method of multiplying which you'll learn too.

Check Your Progress!
Best Of Times
Turn to page 32 and put a tick next to what you have just learned.

Top Tip! If your child struggles with anything, don't worry – let them go at their own pace.

Parents Start Here...

You probably remember long and short division. Your child will learn how to divide using a method known as repeated subtraction, or 'chunking'. Children progress from this method to long and short division only when they are ready. Many children are not taught the more complicated methods until Year Six or even Year Seven.

Divide And Rule

When you divide using pencil and paper you need to know your times tables really well!

You use the multiplication facts you know to take away chunks of a number.
You know that 10 x 15 = 150, so you can take this away first:

262 ÷ 15

Chris: I think that the font is missing from my file, so just wanted to make sure that 'add these numbers' comes out OK in your version.

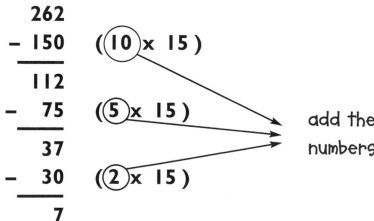

```
    262
  - 150    ( 10 x 15 )
  -----
    112
  -  75    ( 5 x 15 )
  -----
     37
  -  30    ( 2 x 15 )
  -----
      7
```

add these numbers

You managed to get 15 into 262 17 times remainder 7.

Answer: **17 r 7**

The great thing about this method is that you can take off any size chunk you can manage. If you wanted, you could have kept on taking off 15 each time in the question we have just looked at (but it would take ages!).

Use chunking to try these divisions:

536 ÷ 20 =

648 ÷ 30 =

955 ÷ 50 =

FUN FACT!

The Sun is 150 million kilometres from Earth. This is the same as 93 million miles.

TRY THIS

Home Learn

Whenever you do a multiplication or division on paper, think about what the answer might be before you begin and then check your answer with a calculator afterwards.

Check Your Progress!
Divide And Rule

Turn to page 32 and put a tick next to what you have just learned.

Parents Start Here...

During Key Stage Two, children learn how to position and move 2-D shapes on a grid, using co-ordinates to locate them.

And The Point Is...?

Co-ordinates: two numbers that tell you exactly where a point is on a graph.

- Co-ordinates are normally written in brackets, with a comma separating the two numbers e.g. (13, 16).
- On maps, letters may replace the numbers e.g. (J 28).
- The first number always tells you to look along a line.
- The second number always tells you to look up or down a line.

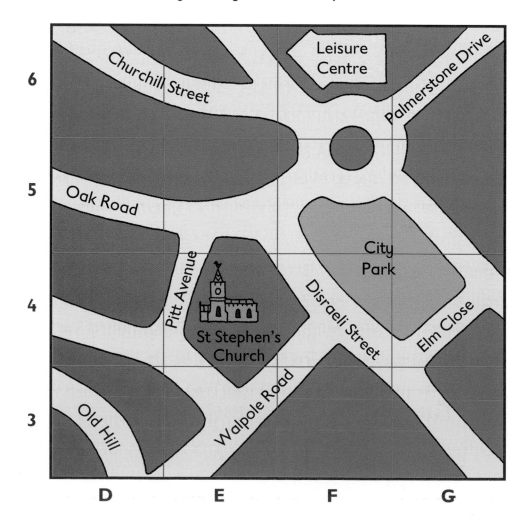

On this map, letters and numbers have been used to label the squares.

1. find 4 on the bottom line and imagine a line going up from it

2. find the 2 on the line going up next and imagine a line coming from it

x marks the spot where two lines meet!

(4,2)

St Stephen's Church is in square (E _____)

The hill found in square (D 3) is called _____

Elm Close is found in square (_____ , _____)

What square contains the Leisure Centre? (_____ , _____)

City Park is found in four squares on the map. Write down the four squares:

(_____ , _____) (_____ , _____) (_____ , _____) (_____ , _____)

FUN FACT!

The Mappa Mundi is one of the oldest surviving maps in the world.
It was drawn in the thirteenth century by a priest at Hereford Cathedral.

TRY THIS

Activity

Ask an adult to show you how maps are labelled using letters and numbers. Atlases, street maps and Ordnance Survey maps all use systems like these.

Check Your Progress!
And The Point Is...?
Turn to page 32 and put a tick next to what you have just learned.

Top Tip!
Bring what your child learns into everyday life – they'll remember it even better.

Parents Start Here...

Rounding numbers helps children in their estimations. It is also a practical tool used in measuring which does not always need to be exact. In this exercise your child is asked to round weights and measures.

Round It Up

You can round numbers up or down.

Rounded to the nearest 100 grams:

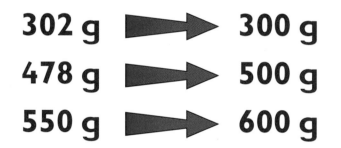

302 g ➡ 300 g

478 g ➡ 500 g

550 g ➡ 600 g

If a number is exactly between two numbers, remember to round up.

Round these weights to the nearest 100 g to get approximate weights:

731g

97g

386g

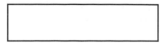

Round these weights to the nearest kilogram to get approximate weights:

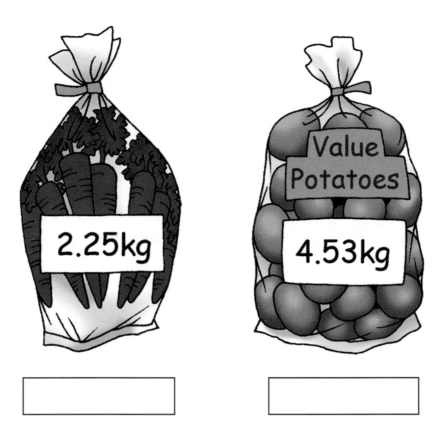

2.25kg

Value Potatoes

4.53kg

FUN FACT!

The greatest weight ever recorded for a human being was 635 kg (100 stone). Jon Minnoch, an American, tried losing weight but eventually died when his heart gave out.

 TRY THIS

Activity

Estimate how much liquid various containers in the kitchen might hold. Use a measuring jug to test your estimations. Your estimates should start getting more accurate quite quickly.

Check Your Progress!

Round It Up

Turn to page 32 and put a tick next to what you have just learned.

Answers

Pages 4–5
True statements:
482 < 890
10,854 = 10,000 + 854
1402 = one thousand four hundred and two
There are lots of answers for these two questions.
Some suggestions are:
Numbers less than 7458 = 4578, 4587, 5478,
5487, 4875
Numbers more than 5874 = 8745, 8754, 7854,
7845, 8457
The smallest number: 4578
The largest number: 8754

Pages 6–7
The string measures 9 cm.
Each side of the triangle measures 3 cm and the
perimeter of the triangle is 9 cm.
The perimeter of the hexagon is 6 x 2 cm = 12 cm
The perimeter of the shape is 16 cm.

Pages 8–9
Multiples of 6 = python
Multiples of 7 = albatross
Multiples of 8 = sequoia

Pages 10–11
The children ran 47 times around the field in total.
James jumped a total distance of 3.51 m
The difference between Julie's and Jasmine's high
jumps was 9 cm.
The difference between 2 minutes 14 seconds and
1 minute 55 seconds is 19 seconds.

Pages 12–13
35 children walk to school.
Five more children walk than go by car.
Cycling was the least popular method of travelling.
The Council might encourage more walking and
use of public transport by making roads safer
(slowing cars down), improving the bus service and
making it cheaper, providing school buses, making
cycle lanes etc.
100 children took part in the survey altogether.

Pages 14–15
A = 3 cm^2
B = 4 cm^2
C = 5 cm^2
D = 5 cm^2

A = 9 cm^2
B = 2 cm^2
C = 4 cm^2
D = 15 cm^2
E = 16 cm^2
F = 8 cm^2

Pages 16–17

$$\frac{1}{4} = \frac{2}{8} \qquad \frac{4}{6} = \frac{2}{3} \qquad \frac{2}{4} = \frac{1}{2} \qquad \frac{1}{2} = \frac{3}{6}$$

$$\frac{5}{10} = \frac{1}{2}$$

$$\frac{3}{10} = 0.3$$

Decimals:
1.8
10.8
6.0

Pages 18–19
736 + 642 = 1378
21.9 + 132. 3 = 154.2
67.3 + 24.1 = 91.4
759 + 16.7 = 775.7
552. 5 + 89.3 = 641.8
3.25 + 8.96 = 12.21

Chunks
963 − 693 = 270
735 − 342 = 393
862 − 97 = 765
1049 − 861 = 188

Pages 20–21

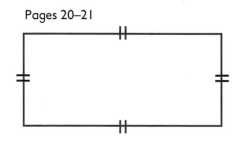

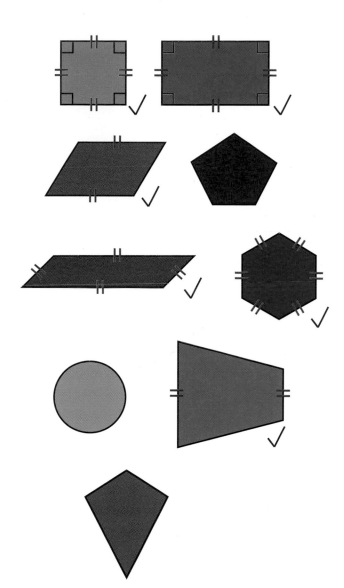

Pages 24–25
536 ÷ 20 = 26 remainder 16
648 ÷ 30 = 21 remainder 18
955 ÷ 50 = 19 remainder 5

Pages 26–27
St Stephen's Church is in square (E 4)
The hill found in square (D 3) is called Old Hill.
Elm Close is found in square (G 4).
Square (F 6) contains the Leisure Centre
City Park is found in:
(F 4)
(G 4)
(F 5)
(G 5)

Pages 28–29
The approximate weights are:
700 g
100 g
400 g
2 kg
5 kg

Pages 22–23

	thousands	hundreds	tens	units
4672	4000	600	70	2
562		500	60	2
66			60	6
486		400	80	6
87			80	7
1023	1000		20	3

If you got this wrong, go back and check your
partitioning and then check each multiplication and the
adding up.

562 x 66 = 37,092

Check Your Progress!

Number Cards .... ☐

String's The Thing .... ☐

Biggest And Best .... ☐

Sports Day .... ☐

School Journeys .... ☐

Square It .... ☐

A Fraction Of... .... ☐

Chopping And Chunking .... ☐

Lines And Corners .... ☐

Best Of Times .... ☐

Divide And Rule .... ☐

And The Point Is...? .... ☐

Round It Up .... ☐